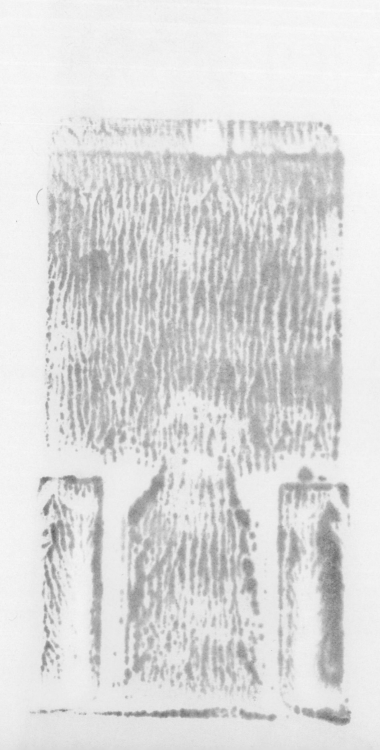

*what*

# COLONEL GLENN

*did all day*

## ROBERT W. HILL

THE JOHN DAY COMPANY
NEW YORK

*Library of Congress Catalogue Card Number: 62-16294*

MANUFACTURED IN THE UNITED STATES OF AMERICA

Fifth Impression

For
M. B. H.

## BEFORE...

Before Colonel John Glenn was fired into space to orbit the earth three times, he and his six fellow astronauts trained for months to make the flight. First, rockets with instruments in them were placed in orbit to learn whether it was safe for living beings. Next, monkeys were sent up in special capsules and brought back. Among them, Able, Baker, Ham, and Enos became famous. Then on May 5, 1961, Alan Shepard became the first American to reach outer space. All the while the astronauts were preparing for space travel. In addition to keeping in good physical condition, they spent many hours in fantastic training machines getting used to the strains caused by flying far beyond the earth at thousands of miles an hour. During the training period they were watched and checked constantly by doctors and scientists. For them it was to be a venture into the unknown. They would be as ready for it as man could be, backed up by a large team which, from top to bottom, gave everything it had to make the Project Mercury space program a success.

An Atlas rocket booster with a Mercury capsule fitted on the top stands on its launching pad. Below, the conditions and flight missions of Project Mercury are set forth. Rocket and capsule were planned to orbit the earth first with instruments, then with animals, then with men.

# PROJECT MERCURY
## ORBITAL FLIGHTS

### CONDITIONS
ALTITUDE...120 MILES
VELOCITY...17,500 MPH
TIME.......4½ HRS, 3 ORBITS

### FLIGHT MISSIONS
INSTRUMENTED CAPSULES
ANIMAL FLIGHTS
MANNED FLIGHTS

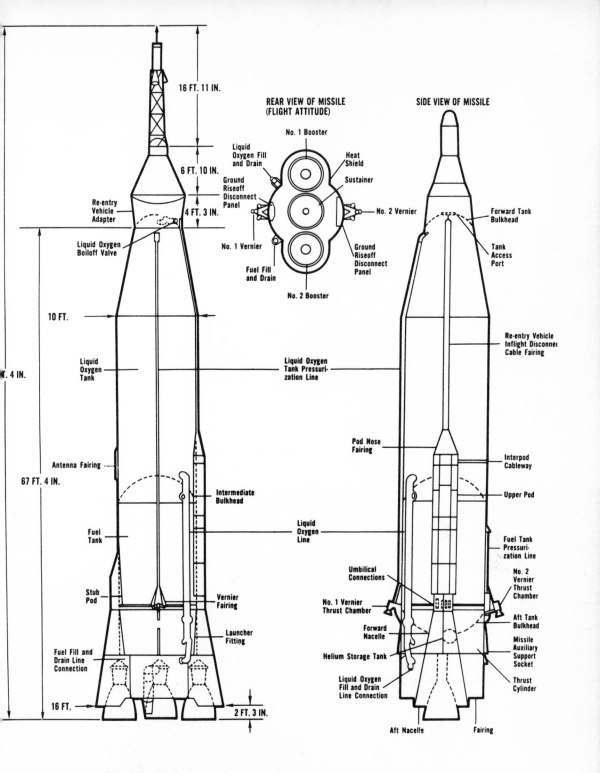

16 FT. 11 IN.

6 FT. 10 IN.

4 FT. 3 IN.

Re-entry Vehicle Adapter

Liquid Oxygen Boiloff Valve

10 FT.

Liquid Oxygen Tank

4 IN.

Antenna Fairing

67 FT. 4 IN.

Fuel Tank

Stub Pod

Fuel Fill and Drain Line Connection

16 FT.

Intermediate Bulkhead

Vernier Fairing

Launcher Fitting

2 FT. 3 IN.

**REAR VIEW OF MISSILE (FLIGHT ATTITUDE)**

No. 1 Booster

Liquid Oxygen Fill and Drain

Ground Riseoff Disconnect Panel

No. 1 Vernier

Fuel Fill and Drain

No. 2 Booster

Heat Shield

Sustainer

No. 2 Vernier

Ground Riseoff Disconnect Panel

**SIDE VIEW OF MISSILE**

Liquid Oxygen Tank Pressurization Line

Liquid Oxygen Line

Pod Nose Fairing

Umbilical Connections

No. 1 Vernier Thrust Chamber

Forward Nacelle

Helium Storage Tank

Liquid Oxygen Fill and Drain Line Connection

Aft Nacelle

Forward Tank Bulkhead

Tank Access Port

Re-entry Vehicle Inflight Disconnect Cable Fairing

Interpod Cableway

Upper Pod

Fuel Tank Pressurization Line

No. 2 Vernier Thrust Chamber

Aft Tank Bulkhead

Missile Auxiliary Support Socket

Thrust Cylinder

Fairing

A scale drawing of the Mercury Atlas rocket showing the main booster, capsule and escape tower sections.

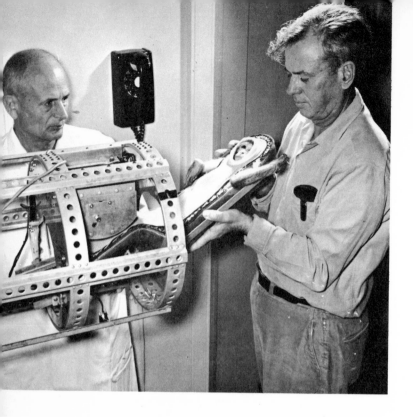

Small monkeys were first used to test the effects of space travel on living beings. Here doctors at the University of Texas place monkeys in a special frame and container to protect them in flight. The University has a colony of monkeys for just such use.

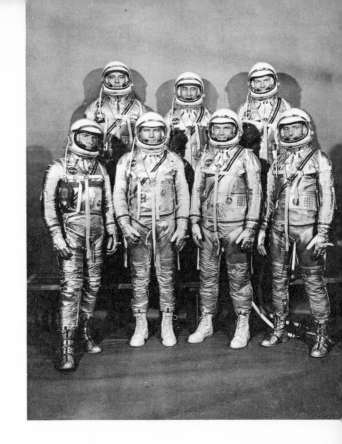

The seven fliers selected finally to make America's man-in-space flights. All are military test pilots with thousands of hours in the air. In their space suits, left to right, front row: Walter Schirra, Donald "Deke" Slayton, John Glenn, and Scott Carpenter; back row: Alan Shepard, Virgil "Gus" Grissom, and Donald Cooper. They were also chosen for their fine physical condition. Below, with a model of the Mercury Atlas, left to right, front row: Grissom, Carpenter, Slayton, and Cooper; back row: Shepard, Schirra, and Glenn.

Below, Colonel Glenn keeps himself in shape by running in the wet sand along the ocean near Cape Canaveral. In addition to physical fitness programs, the astronauts spent hours in the classroom and learning to operate special training machines able to do what a Mercury capsule would do 100 miles above the earth, going more than 17,500 miles an hour. In this way the astronauts learned to control a spacecraft without the dangers of real flight. Among the special trainers were the multiple-axis machine, the Mastiff vertical test, high-pressure chambers, and centrifuges.

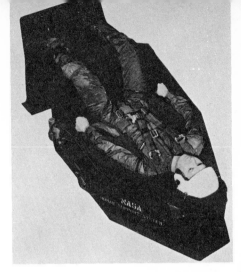

Above is a human support couch made to take heavy shocks. The astronaut lies on his back during blast-off and landing. Right, an astronaut "flies" in a Mastiff vertical trainer. He can make it put him in any position. Below, a multiple-axis space test machine in a wind tunnel.

To see how an astronaut takes the strains of space flight, he is whirled in a circle at high speeds by a centrifuge. Above, one enters the gondola on a long boom. It will whirl him like a stone at the end of a string. Below, Deke Slayton rides the centrifuge. The faster he spins the greater the strain, called G (gravity) forces.

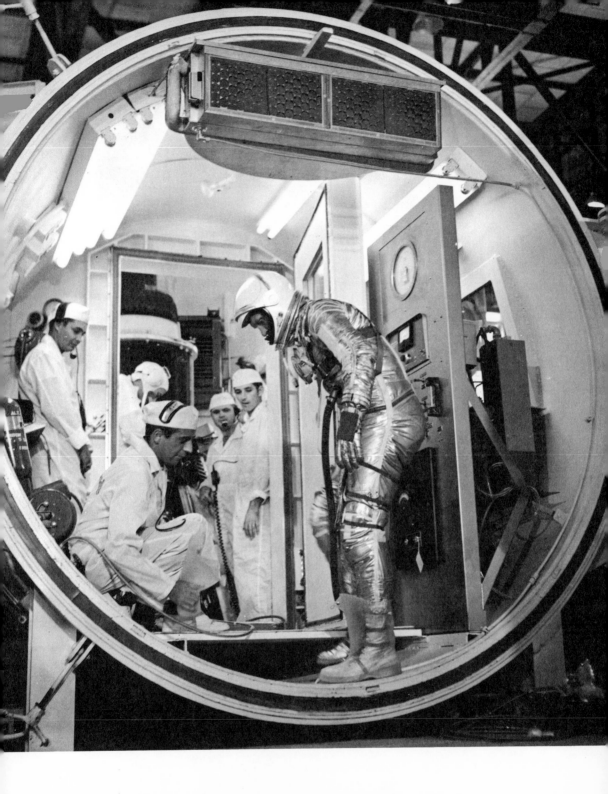

Colonel Glenn, in training on the ground, enters a high-pressure chamber to see how well he can take the great forces of space flight.

Astronaut Carpenter runs through a ground test flight in the Friendship 7 capsule. Below, he practices getting out of the capsule and into a life raft. Here he trains in a swimming pool. To get used to high waves the ocean also was used.

To learn how a launching is carried out, Astronauts Cooper and Slayton watch a countdown in the blockhouse of the control center at Cape Canaveral. An Atlas-D rocket is about to be fired. Below, in Mercury Control, technicians monitor the launching.

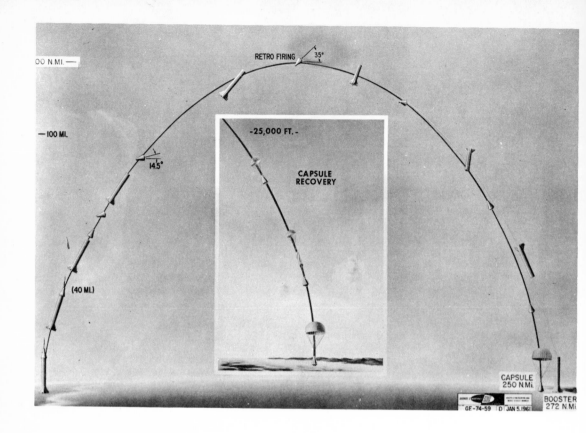

The first American fired into space was Astronaut Alan Shepard, May 5, 1961. Above is a drawing of his flight. He went up 115 miles and landed in the Atlantic 302 miles from Cape Canaveral. He was not meant to go into orbit. Below, another drawing shows the stages of his flight.

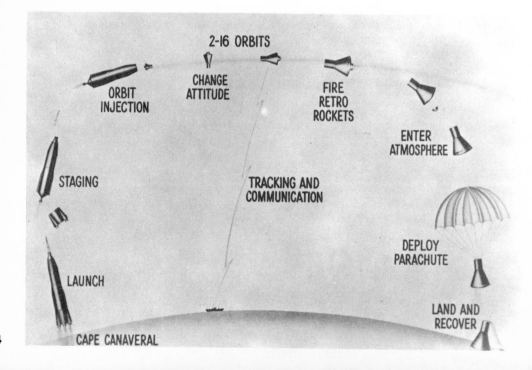

A helicopter hoists Alan Shepard aboard after he has left his capsule in the Atlantic Ocean. The spacecraft is floating at the lower left. He grinned and said, "Man, what a ride!"

After landing in the ocean, Astronaut Shepard was taken by helicopter to the aircraft carrier *Lake Champlain* nearby. Above, Shepard on the carrier flight deck. Behind him is the ship's commanding officer, Captain Ralph Weymouth. Below, astronaut "Gus" Grissom prepares to enter spacecraft Liberty Bell 7. He rose 118 miles at 5,310 miles an hour, also in suborbital flight.

Mercury capsule Friendship 7 is hoisted to the top of the Atlas rocket to be made ready for firing. In the gantry is the Atlas booster, number 1090.

With the capsule fixed to the Atlas booster, an astronaut practices fitting into it high above Cape Canaveral.

Colonel Glenn lifts himself into Friendship 7
spacecraft during pre-launch checkout activities.

Because of the very limited room inside the Mercury capsule, the astronaut gets a helping hand from a technician as he fits himself into the human support couch.

A technician puts the last touches to United States markings on Friendship 7 as it sits in the gantry. It is sealed against dust and damp until
Colonel Glenn enters it for blast-off.

Above, the Mercury Atlas, with the giant steel frame gantry along-
side, as it would look shortly before launching. A last-minute check of
weather maps is made below by top space scientists Hugh Dryden,
Walter Williams and Robert Gilruth.

Colonel John Glenn looks to the future on the eve of his try for a three-orbit flight around the world. All is now ready for the countdown and the command to lift off.

# DURING...

Long before sunrise on the morning of February 20, 1962, Lieutenant Colonel John H. Glenn, Marine combat and test pilot, was awakened. For weeks bad weather or small troubles with the Mercury Atlas rocket system had caused his orbital space flight to be called off. He was to try again. Eager and smiling, he ate a special breakfast and got into his space suit. In the dark he rode to the launch pad and entered the spacecraft called Friendship 7, high on the top of an Atlas rocket.

Then the countdown began. At 9:21 that morning, hours later, with the whole world waiting, he was blasted into outer space. His calm voice counted off the last seconds: "... three, two, one, lift off!" The rocket pushed him through the earth's atmosphere. Next, his capsule was parted from the booster and he was in orbit 100 miles above the earth. He sped three times around it at more than 17,500 miles an hour. For almost five hours he was weightless, but able to control his spacecraft himself by a system called "fly by wire." At the end of his 80,000-mile trip he came back into the earth's atmosphere in a ball of fire and was picked up by a destroyer. When his parachute opened to set Friendship 7 down in the ocean he said of it, "That's probably the prettiest ol' sight you ever saw." His historic flight was over.

On the morning of the launch, hours before sunrise, Colonel Glenn eats
a light breakfast of steak, potatoes, toast, jam, and orange juice.

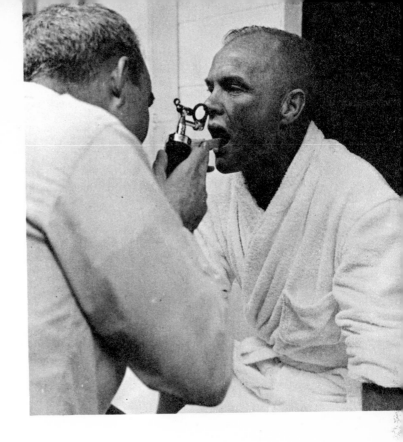

A last-minute checkup is given the astronaut before he "suits up." Below, electronic sensors are placed on Colonel Glenn's body by Dr. William Douglas. They will send signals back to Cape Canaveral to show how he feels in space.

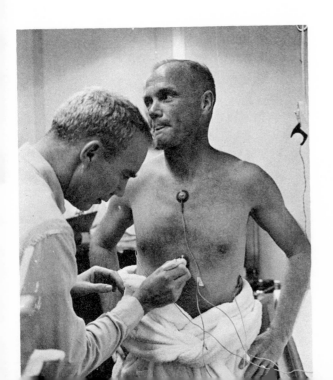

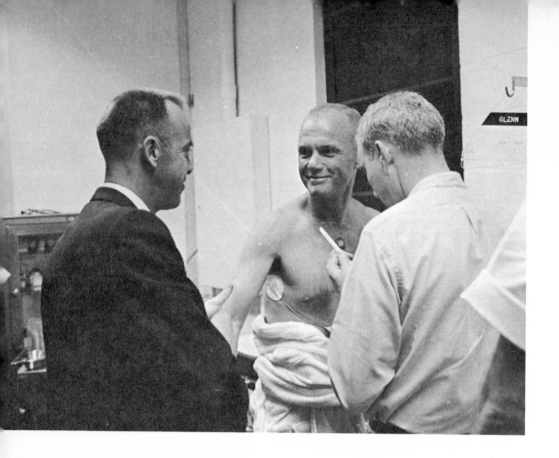

Astronaut Shepard shakes Colonel Glenn's hand and wishes him good luck. Below, the flight gear is made ready, including suit, helmet face shield, and special gloves.

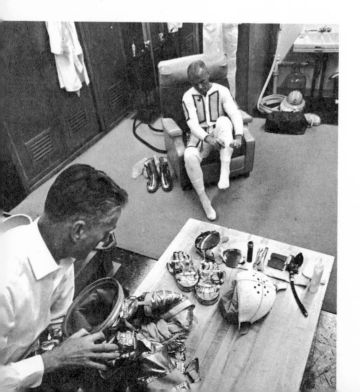

The gloves that guarded the hands of Colonel Glenn on his three-orbit flight. They have laces at the backs, lock rings to fasten them to the sleeves of his spacesuit, and electric lights in the tips of the first two fingers of each hand. The lights helped him see the instrument panel when he was on the dark side of the earth.

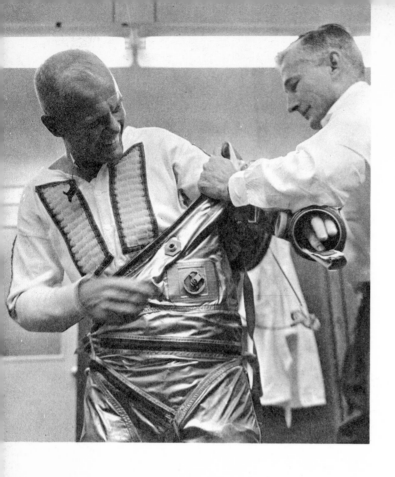

Colonel Glenn, aided by flight gear specialist Joe
Schmitt, dons his space suit and special harness.

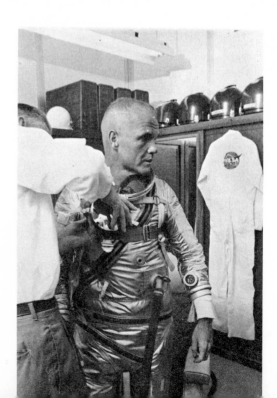

Fully dressed for his flight, the astronaut walks to a large trailer that will take him to the launch pad and Friendship 7. In his left hand he carries a small air-conditioning unit to keep him comfortable until blast-off. An elevator in the gantry took him up to the capsule.

Atop the Atlas booster, in the black of early morning, Colonel Glenn approaches the spacecraft hatch.

Astronaut Glenn squeezes into the spacecraft. The count-down has begun and final pre-launch activities are under way.

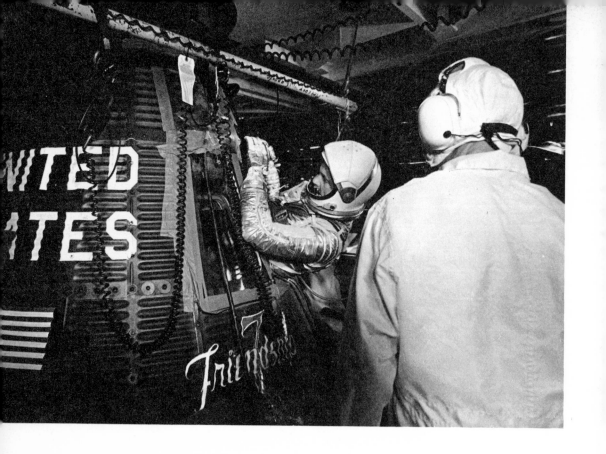

Colonel Glenn as he works his way into the Mercury capsule.
Below, he is ready to lift off when the countdown reaches zero.

In the control blockhouse Astronaut Alan Shepard signals lift-off as the countdown clock at his right reaches zero hours, zero minutes, and zero seconds. Below, Shepard talks with Colonel Glenn as he roars through the atmosphere.

On the opposite page, with the countdown completed and the gantry moved back, John Glenn's Atlas rocket, blasting fire and smoke, lifts slowly and surely from its launch pad. It gains altitude and he is under way.

A view of Glenn's rocket as it lifts off, seen from atop a Saturn gantry, looking down the heavy launch road. Below, thousands of "bird watchers" jam the beaches around Cape Canaveral to see the launch. The fiery rocket exhaust can be seen in the upper left-hand corner.

U.P.I.

An elderly woman strikes a prayerful pose as she watches the blast-off of the Atlas rocket with Colonel Glenn riding the space capsule at its nose.

Below is a part of the radio voice messages between Colonel Glenn and Mercury Control at Cape Canaveral the morning of the blast-off. CC stands for Cape Canaveral. P is for pilot. The first group of numerals shows the time in hours, minutes, and seconds following the countdown. The next figures indicate how long each conversation lasted in seconds.

|  |  |  |  |
|---|---|---|---|
|  | CC | . . . 8, 7, 6, 5, 4, 3, 2, 1, 0 [lift off!] |
| 00 00 03 | 4.0 | P | Roger. The clock is operating. We're under way. |
| 00 00 07 | 1.5 | CC | Hear [you] loud and clear. |
| 00 00 08 | 2.0 | P | Roger. We're programming in roll okay. |
| 00 00 13 | 3.5 | P | Little bumpy along about here. |
| 00 00 48 | 2.5 | P | Have some vibration coming up here now. |
| 00 00 52 | 2.0 | CC | Roger. Reading you loud and clear. |
| 00 00 55 | 4.0 | P | Roger. Coming into high Q [vibration] a little bit; and a contrail went by the window, or something there. |
| 00 01 00 | 0.5 | CC | Roger. |
| 00 01 12 | 3.0 | P | We're smoothing out some now, getting out of the vibration area. |
| 00 01 16 | 3.0 | CC | Roger. You're through max. Q. Your flight path is . . . |
| 00 01 19 | 3.2 | P | Roger. Feels good, through max. Q and smoothing out real fine. |
| 00 01 31 | 2.0 | P | Sky looking very dark outside. |

| | | | | |
|---|---|---|---|---|
| 00 02 07 | 5.0 | CC | Roger.  Reading you loud and clear.  Flight path looked good. Pitch, 25. Stand by . . . |
| 00 02 12 | 8.0 | P | Roger.  The [escape] tower fired; could not see the tower go.  I saw the smoke go by the window. |
| 00 02 27 | 3.0 | P | Still have about one and one-half G's.  Programming.  Over. |
| 00 02 36 | 7.5 | P | There, the tower went right then. Have the tower in sight way out. Could see the tower go. Jettison tower is green. |
| 00 04 08 | 10.5 | P | Friendship Seven.  Fuel 103-101 [percent], oxygen 78-100, amps 25, cabin pressure holding steady at 58. |
| 00 04 20 | 5.0 | CC | Roger.  Reading you loud and clear.  Seven, Cape is Go; we're standing by for you. |
| 00 04 25 | 16.5 | P | Roger.  Cape is Go and I am Go. Capsule is in good shape . . . All systems are Go. |
| 00 05 12 | 5.0 | P | Roger.  Zero-G, and I feel fine. Capsule is turning around. |
| 00 05 18 | 1.8 | P | Oh, that view is tremendous! |
| 00 05 21 | 1.5 | CC | Roger.  Turnaround has started. |
| 00 05 23 | 7.0 | P | Roger.  The capsule is turning around and I can see the booster during turnaround just a couple of hundred yards behind me.  It was beautiful. |
| 00 05 30 | 4.5 | CC | Roger, Seven.  You have a Go, at least seven orbits. |
| 00 05 35 | 4.5 | P | Roger.  Understand Go for at least seven orbits. |

In Mercury Control at Cape Canaveral, launch experts watch the big board. The bright light, lower right corner of the world map, shows Glenn's capsule leaving Australia at night on its first orbit. There the people of Perth turned on their lights for him to see. Below, a group of doctors keep a close watch on the astronaut's physical condition during the flight.

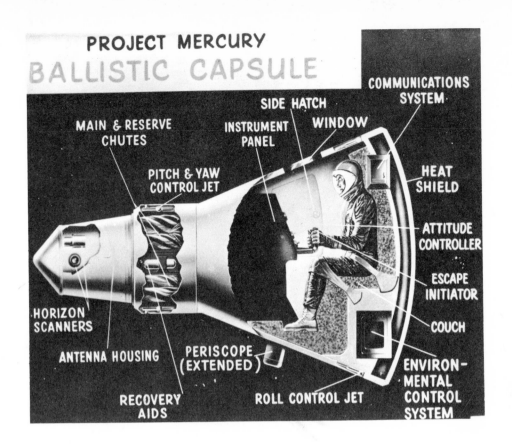

**PROJECT MERCURY**
**BALLISTIC CAPSULE**

MAIN & RESERVE CHUTES

SIDE HATCH

INSTRUMENT PANEL

WINDOW

COMMUNICATIONS SYSTEM

PITCH & YAW CONTROL JET

HEAT SHIELD

ATTITUDE CONTROLLER

ESCAPE INITIATOR

HORIZON SCANNERS

COUCH

ANTENNA HOUSING

PERISCOPE (EXTENDED)

RECOVERY AIDS

ROLL CONTROL JET

ENVIRON-MENTAL CONTROL SYSTEM

Above is a sketch of Friendship 7 and its main sections. Below is a sketch of the capsule's instrument panel. The top center section shows the capsule's roll, pitch, and yaw gauges. The scope at its lower left shows what point of the world it is over.

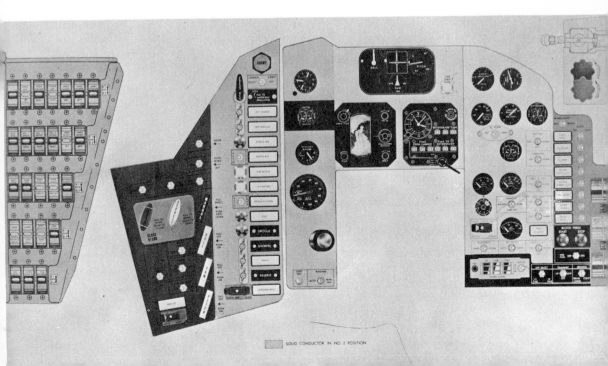

SOLID CONDUCTOR IN NO. 2 POSITION

Astronaut John Glenn in space as his picture was taken automatically. Here he is weightless, traveling at 17,500 miles an hour.

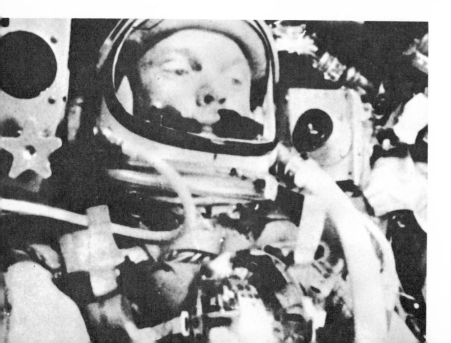

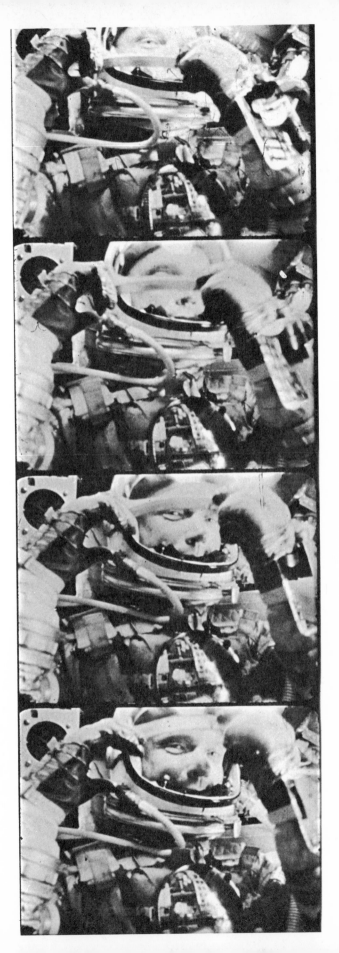

Colonel Glenn raises the face-
plate of his space helmet while
in orbit and eats from a plastic
tube filled with applesauce.

A photograph of clouds over the Pacific taken by Colonel Glenn on his first orbit. He was then 100 miles above the earth, going 17,500 miles an hour. Below, North Africa as it looked to him. He was able to see great dust storms that looked like forest fires.

A view of the Florida coast taken by Colonel Glenn as he started his second orbit. Below, one of the four sunsets he saw that day. He said, "They were most impressive . . . brilliantly colored hues from the sun to the horizon." Note the curve of the horizon.

At the end of his third orbit Colonel Glenn fired retro-rockets to slow the space capsule down before it came back into the earth's atmosphere. For a while it was feared that the space-craft might burn up. He was ringed by the heat of re-entry. Then he was heard yelling, "Boy. That was a real fireball!" He next fired out a parachute, like the one on the opposite page, that let him down gently into the Atlantic Ocean. The capsule was so hot that it sent up a cloud of steam as it touched the water. It had been in flight for 4 hours and 56 minutes.

A number of United States Navy ships were waiting near the point where he was to land. One of them was the aircraft carrier *Randolph.* On it were helicopters and skin divers to help him out of the capsule and take him back to the carrier.

Because the astronaut took over the controls and made a number of last-minute changes in the flight of Friendship 7, he landed nearer the destroyer U.S.S. *Noa* than to the aircraft carrier. It picked him up and radioed to all the world the word that John Glenn was safely aboard and feeling fine.

1

2

3

4

5

6

After the spacecraft has re-entered the earth's atmosphere, the astronaut fires out a parachute. First the big canopy is pulled out of the capsule by a drogue chute, then it opens and lowers the spacecraft into the ocean.

The spacecraft Friendship 7 with John Glenn inside floats in the Atlantic Ocean near Grand Turk Island. The U.S.S. *Noa* picked up the capsule 21 minutes after it landed and reported the astronaut in good condition.

Skin divers aboard the carrier *Randolph* wait near their "chopper" to help Astronaut Glenn out of Friendship 7 once it has landed in the water. Above the door is a movie camera, and a sling to hoist him aboard. Because the *Noa* reached Glenn first, the skin divers were not needed. Below, crewmen of the *Noa* hold a sign welcoming Colonel Glenn as their destroyer races to pick him up.

NOAS MEN WELCOME GLENN

U.S.S.NOA (DD·841)

Crewmen of the *Noa* get ready to lift Friendship 7 to its deck. A special boom was built to grip the top of the capsule without denting it. Below, Colonel Glenn, who blasted a hatch open in the capsule and crawled out, helps fasten the spacecraft to the deck.

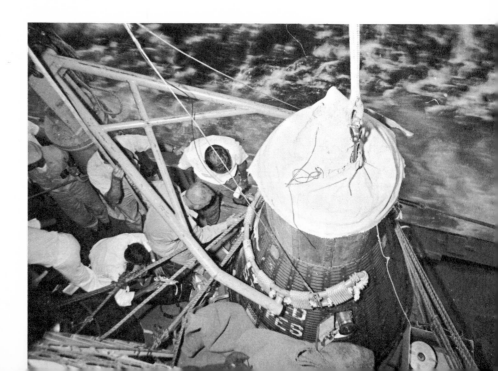

Aboard the U.S.S. *Noa*, the Friendship 7 spacecraft is secured to the deck by strong lines as Colonel Glenn looks on. On the horizon is the fourth sunset the astronaut saw that day.

In a cabin aboard the destroyer *Noa,* Colonel Glenn telephones his wife in Virginia to tell her he is safe. Below, before leaving the *Noa,* he packs the space suit he wore on his three-orbit flight around the earth.

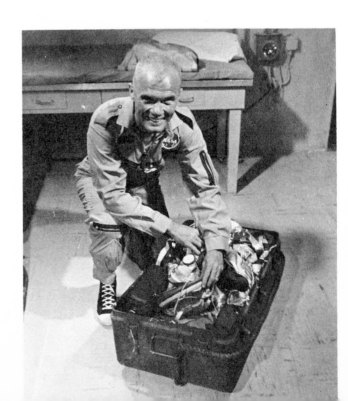

John Glenn is hoisted by a Navy helicopter from the deck of the *Noa* to be flown to the aircraft carrier *Randolph* to begin his debriefing. He is lifted by cable through the trap doors at the bottom of the chopper and they are then closed.

Aboard the *Randolph* members of the crew wait on the flight deck for
the helicopter bringing Colonel Glenn from the *Noa*. Behind them a
number of planes are parked, including three jet fighters. Below, in
the wardroom of the carrier, the astronaut tells of the flight he called
"a successful outing."

# AFTER...

As Colonel Glenn in Friendship 7 circled the earth, 135,000,000 Americans watched and listened and read of his flight. The eyes and ears of all the world were with him. At the White House in Washington, President Kennedy also was thrilled by the news that the astronaut had been brought back safely. The President said, "This is a new ocean, and I believe that the United States must sail on it . . . second to none."

To Colonel Glenn, his flight was but one small part in a success that the President said went "far beyond our own time and our own country." The dangers the astronaut had met in outer space were past, but he now faced a new test. It was a time of blaring bands, of ticker-tape parades, of political offers, jobs, and quick rewards, speeches, medals, and national honors. But Colonel Glenn never lost his head. He was as calm and modest as he had been in flight. He pointed out that it only happened to be his turn to make the first manned orbital flight, and that his place was with the space program. Then, as soon as the shouting had died down, he went back to work on future space flights with the other astronauts.

A smiling, happy Colonel John Glenn relaxes on Grand Turk Island, where he continued debriefing for 48 hours. He was flown there by jet from the aircraft carrier *Randolph*.

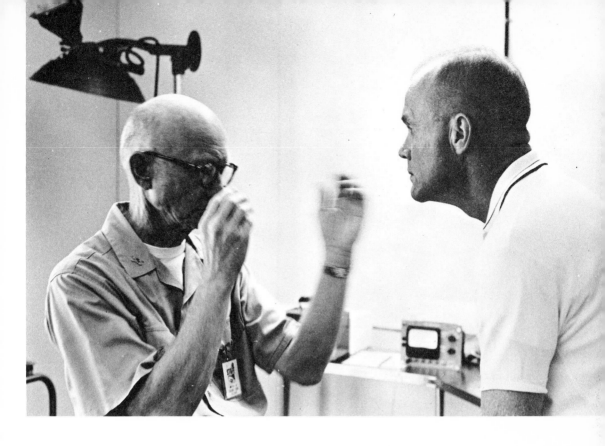

A Navy doctor checks the astronaut's eyesight. Below, electronic sensors are placed on Colonel Glenn's head to record his reactions to the space flight. The tests showed him to be in perfect health.

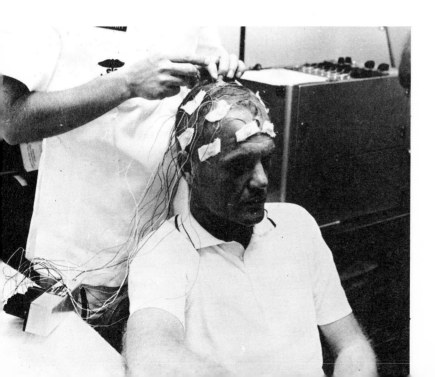

Colonel Glenn's family at their home in Virginia. With their mother, Anna, are Lyn, fourteen, and Dave, sixteen. When asked how they felt about their father's flight, they said they were glad he was back safely, but that they knew all along he would do it.

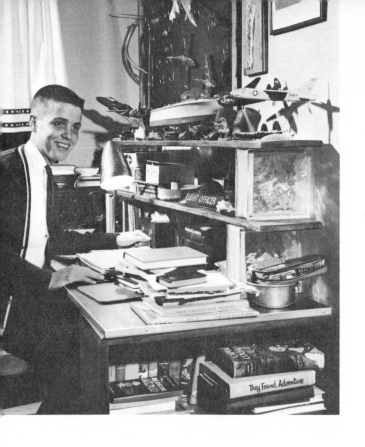

Dave Glenn is much like his father. He is interested in boating, water skiing, and flying. Here he is seen at his desk at home. Around him are some of his books and models of Navy planes. Below, Lyn sits by the fireplace. She considers herself a typical teen-ager.

Three days after his space flight, Colonel Glenn is awarded the NASA medal by President Kennedy. It is the highest honor given by the National Aeronautics and Space Administration, which was in charge of Project Mercury.

Colonel Glenn speaks to a joint session of Congress. In the front row are the Supreme Court judges. The astronaut explained that he was only one of a great many who had made his flight a success. Below, he talks with President Kennedy and Vice-President Johnson on the steps of the White House before a Washington parade.

New York City gave Colonel Glenn the greatest welcome in its history. Four million people cheered him as he rode with his wife in an open car along Wall Street and up Fifth Avenue. From office buildings, 3,474 tons of paper fluttered down on them in the ticker-tape parade.

Home at last. Colonel and Mrs. John Glenn ride down Main Street in his home town. Here in New Concord, Ohio, he grew up. In a way, it was the end of one of the greatest and longest trips in American history.

## About the Author

Robert W. Hill is an editor and writer with special training and interest in aviation. He actively maintains his pilot's license, which he has held for many years. He has edited an anthology of writings about flight, generally considered the best ever published, a handbook on rocketry, and numerous other books about aviation and about the sea.

COMPLETED

INVENTORY 74

INVENTORY 1983